THE AWARE BEARS
We're on Our Own
A CHILDREN'S GUIDE TO SAFETY WHILE ALONE AT HOME

by
JEANNE L. LOKAR
Teacher
Gananda Central School, Walworth, NY

Project Director
JOHN DOWNEY

Project Coordinator
LOIS COHEN

Series Consultants

FRANK MACHOVEC, PhD
Licensed Clinical Psychologist
Director, Center for the Study of the Self
Richmond, VA

ALAN D. FRANKEL
Adjunct Professor, Westchester Community College
Valhalla, NY

THERESA STRELEC
North Castle Public Library
Armonk, NY

Illustrations by
KEVIN KLEIN

OCEANA EDUCATIONAL COMMUNICATIONS
DOBBS FERRY, NY

J362.7
Lo

2109

Contents

Introduction: **The Aware Bears**

Have you ever seen a Panda before? May-Ling and Li Bear are Pandas. Pandas are cuddly, black and white bearlike mammals. They live in the bamboo forests of China. Pandas can be very big. They can grow to 5 feet tall and weigh 350 pounds. Pandas eat bamboo, roots, leaves, and flowers. They hold food with their feet and paws.

May-Ling and Li Bear are brother and sister. They live in a new place that is different from the bamboo forests of China. Living in this new place is fun. May-Ling and Li can meet new friends. They can go to school.

Like many other children, May-Ling and Li Bear need to be *Aware Bears*. Like Mommies and Daddies who love and care for their children, *Aware Bears* must love and care for each other and their friends. *Aware Bears* know what is good and what is bad. They know what is nice and what is not nice. An *Aware Bear* knows what to do when Mommy and Daddy cannot be there to help.

Be an *Aware Bear* and always be safe and well.

Li = Lee

May-Ling and Li Bear were on their way
home from school one day.

"Let's run," said May-Ling, "I am
hungry!"

"Sure!" said Li racing toward home.

Soon they were home, safe and well.

The telephone started to ring.

"I will get it," called May-Ling as she
rushed to the telephone.

"Is your mommy home?" asked the voice
on the telephone.

"She's busy now," said May-Ling; "could I take a message?"

After taking the message, May-Ling hung up the telephone.

"Why did you say Mommy was busy? You know she's at work!" said Li.

"Silly Li! That's not right! Remember, we must be careful not to tell anyone that Mommy is not at home."

"I'm hungry," said May-Ling.

Soon, May-Ling and Li were fixing a tasty snack: peanut butter-banana sandwiches.

"Let's make popcorn, too!" said Li.

"Silly Li! That's not right! Remember, no cooking until Mommy gets home."

"Why?" asked Li.

"Lot's of reasons," May-Ling answered.

"Think of the mess Mommy might come home to! And, what's worse, if we were not very, very careful, there could even be a FIRE! Imagine the smoke! The damage!"

"You sure are an aware bear, May-Ling."

13

While May-Ling and Li were eating the last of their sandwiches, the doorbell rang.

"I will get it!" Li shouted as he dashed to the door.

"Remember to look out the window first.
Be sure it is someone we know before you
open the door," said May-Ling. "If you
cannot see who it is, ask who it is."

Seeing friends, Li opened the door. It was Polly and Peter, their fox friends from school.

"Could you come to our house to play?"
asked Polly.

"Our Mom said you could come to play.
Call your Mother to let her know where
you will be."

After talking to Mother on the phone,

May-Ling and Li played with their friends on the sidewalk by Peter's house. They began jumping, hopping, and skipping rope.

Soon it was May-Ling's turn to jump.
Suddenly, there was a thump! And a yelp!

"Ouch!" bellowed May-Ling, dropping to the sidewalk, "I've hurt my knee."

"Let's rush to the doctor," yelled Li.

"Silly Li! That's not right! Remember, for help, we must call Mommy's friend, Mrs. Rabbit. She lives close by, and knows a lot about helping."

Li rushed inside to call Mrs. Rabbit.

In a flash, Mrs. Rabbit hopped over to wash and bandage May-Ling's knee.

"That was not so bad after all," Mrs. Rabbit said.

Just then, Mother came home.

"And have you had a good day?" she
asked as she hugged her little bears.

"Oh yes, Mommy. And we have not been
one bit silly at all!"

Are You An Aware Bear?

1 | What rule did May-Ling remember when she talked to the stranger on the phone?

2 | Why is this a good rule?

3 | What snack did the aware bears have after school?

4 | Why is it a good snack to have when Mother or Father are not home?

5 | What are other good snacks to have after school? Why might these be good snacks?

6 | Why did Polly and Peter Fox not play inside at the bear's house?

7 | Where did the friends play? What did they play?

8 | What happened to May-Ling while they were playing?

9 | What had the aware bears' mother told them to do in case of an accident?

10 | What would you do if your parents were not home and you got hurt?

11 | Why did the aware bears tell Mother they "have not been one bit silly"?

Aware Bear Word List

aware
banana
bellowed
butter
damage
dashed
doctor
doorbell
dropping
flash
group
hopping
imagine
knee
message
mom

mommy
mother
ouch
pair
sandwiches
sidewalk
smoke
snapped
tasty
telephone
thump
toward
worse
yelp

KEVIN KLEIN
The Aware Bears "Youth-for-Youth" Illustrator

Sixteen-year-old **Kevin Klein** is a student at Hastings (NY) High School. In 1986, he was awarded first place in a Congressional Arts Caucus-sponsored art contest for high school students. In 1985, **Kevin** was one of only 150 New York students to be accepted into New York State's Summer School of the Arts Program at Fredonia College. **Kevin's** painting, *Portrait of Jenny,* is on display in Washington DC's Capitol Building as part of the Congressional Art Exhibit. One of his other works is on permanent display at the Albright-Knox Museum in Buffalo. Since 1978, **Kevin** has studied with artist Louise Freedman.

Kevin was selected from a group of youth artists to illustrate *The Aware Bears* series. During an introductory interview, each young illustrator presented his or her portfolio, discussed feelings on the need for safety education, and how he or she would approach the illustrating of *The Aware Bears* series. After these initial interviews, select artists were commissioned to illustrate a scene in watercolor. Each artist was given a detailed set of written specifications to illustrate. **Kevin** was selected on the basis of his ability to carry out these instructions, and for "bringing to life" May-Ling and Li Bear: THE AWARE BEARS.